JOHANNES BRAHMS

AKADEMISCHE FESTOUVERTÜRE
ACADEMIC FESTIVAL OVERTURE

Op. 80

Edited by
Richard Clarke

Ernst Eulenburg Ltd

London · Mainz · Madrid · New York · Paris · Prague · Tokyo · Toronto · Zürich

CONTENTS

The text of the present edition of Brahms's *Academic Festival Overture*
Op.80 is based on *Johannes Brahms: Sämtliche Werke. Ausgabe der Gesellschaft
der Musikfreunde in Wien* edited by Hans Gál (Leipzig, 1926).

Ernst Eulenburg Ltd
48 Great Marlborough Street
London W1F 7BB

PREFACE

On 11 March 1879 Breslau's Friedrich Wilhelm University conferred an honorary doctorate on Brahms. The award described the composer, who was then living in Vienna, as 'artis musicae severioris in Germania nunc princeps' (now the leading exponent of the stricter art of music in Germany),[1] the teaching staff evidently assuming that the composer would be sufficiently flattered as to find some way of expressing his gratitude for the honour that had been bestowed on him. There was even talk of a 'doctoral symphony' or a festive cantata.[2] In the event, however, more than a year was to pass before Brahms gratified their expectations, and it was not until 31 March 1880 that he wrote to the University to announce that he would travel to Breslau early the next year 'for a doctoral carousel with a game of skittles'.[3]

Even though we have no documentary evidence to support such a suggestion, it seems likely that by this date Brahms already had in his head certain ideas concerning his new work, which he proceeded to set down on paper during his 1880 summer vacation at Bad Ischl in the Salzkammergut. It is striking that in writing the work, to which he gave the title *Academic Festival Overture*, he had recourse to none of the orchestral genres with which he was familiar, be they serenade, variations or symphony. Instead, he fell back on what for him was the completely new medium of the concert overture 'à la Weber, Cherubini and Mendelssohn'.[4] This was a medium that had symphonic ambitions but which permitted the composer a certain formal freedom. In this respect the genre came close to Brahms's idea of what his new work should be like: central to it were musical quotations from student songs that were universally popular at this period. This was a point that

Brahms described jokingly in a letter to his publisher, in which he referred to the piece as 'a very jolly potpourri of student songs à la Suppé'.[5]

Brahms used four song tunes that he almost certainly found in the 1861 edition of the *Commers-Buch für den deutschen Studenten* (Book of Drinking Songs for the German Student), a copy of which he owned:[6]

(1) the tune of the student song 'Wir hatten gebauet ein stattliches Haus' (We had built a magnificent house) that is quoted episodically in bars 63ff.:

(2) the central section of the song 'Alles schweige! Jeder neige ernsten Tönen nun sein Ohr!' (Let all fall silent! Let each man lend an ear to earnest tones), which includes the words 'Hört, ich sing das Lied der Lieder' (Listen, I am singing the song of songs) that are developed in the second subject-group in bars 129ff.:

Quoted by Max Kalbeck, *Johannes Brahms*, 4 Vols., 2nd edn (Berlin, 1912), iii.251–2
Kalbeck, *Johannes Brahms* (note 1), iii.251
Kalbeck, *Johannes Brahms* (note 1), iii.251
Kalbeck, *Johannes Brahms* (note 1), iii.266, note 31

5 Kalbeck, *Johannes Brahms* (note 1), iii.266, note 19
6 See Christian Martin Schmidt, *Reclams Musikführer Johannes Brahms* (Stuttgart, 1994), 82

(3) the melody of the freshmen's song 'Was kommt dort von der Höh' (What is coming there from the heights?), cited as an episode in bars 156ff.:

Lebhaft

Was kommt dort von der Höh', was kommt dort von der Höh'? was kommt dort von der le-der-nen Höh', ça ça le-der-nen Höh', was kommt dort von der Höh'?

(4) the melody of arguably the best-known of all German student songs, 'Gaudeamus igitur', which is quoted at the climax of the coda in bars 379ff. ('Maestoso'):

Feierlich

Gau-de-a-mus i-gi tur, ju-ve-nes dum su_mus; post ju-cun-dum ju-ven-tu-tem, post mo-les-tam se-nec-tu-tem nos ha-be-bit_ hu-mus, nos ha-be-bit_ hu-mus.

This underlying idea seems to have less to do with a solemn ceremony at which faculty rectors and members of the teaching staff were to bestow an honorary doctorate on the composer than with the more carefree aspects of student life. At first sight, it certainly gives us pause for thought, causing even Max Kalbeck to write in his life of Brahms:

Superficially, the overture, which has more to say to the student body than to their teachers, might be regarded as a prank played by a composer fundamentally opposed to all stereotypical, periwigged nonsense. And it is impossible to exclude the notion that the composer, who had finally been forced to don a doctor's cap and gown, allowed himself a joke at the expense of the learned professors striding on to the platform in all their finery – the thought of summoning them into the concert hall and introducing them to the strains of a freshmen's song, before sending them home with 'Gaudeamus igitur' ringing in their ears, is by no means out of the question, given his roguish sense of humour.[7]

But on closer examination, the piece proves to contain potential allusions to the actual occasion for which it was composed. To take an example: the opening line of the song that Brahms chose for his first quotation and that was familiar to every contemporary listener – 'We had built a magnificent house' – may be seen as a reference to the re-establishment and expansion of Breslau University following the merger of the old Leopoldina and the Viadrina of Frankfurt an der Oder in 1811, while the second quotation – 'Let all fall silent', from which Brahms took only the original music to the words 'Listen, I am singing the song of songs' for his second subject-group – could be interpreted as a gesture of gratitude on the part of the overture's author. Finally, it may have been not so much the opening strophe of 'Gaudeamus igitur' that Brahms had in mind when he chose this song for the hymn-like conclusion of his overture as the fourth strophe, which contains the lines: 'Vivat academia / Vivant professores / Vivat membrum quodlibet / Vivat membra quaelibet / Semper sint in flore' (Long live the academy, long live its professors, long live each member and each department, may they flourish for ever).[8]

Brahms's Op. 80 received its successful first performance in Breslau on 4 January 1881 under the composer's own direction. The programme also included his *Tragic Overture* Op. 81, the *Academic Festival Overture's* companion piece, these two overtures from the same period showing different aspects of the composer – 'One of them weeps, the other one laughs.'[9] The fact that the overture that expresses laughter entered

7 Kalbeck, *Johannes Brahms* (note 1), iii.252
8 L. Benda (ed.), *Buch der Lieder: 262 beliebte Volksweisen aus alter und neuer Zeit* (Braunschweig, n.d. [c.1910])
9 Thus Brahms in a letter to Carl Reinecke of 7 October 1880; see *Johannes Brahms Briefwechsel*, ed. Deutsche Brahms-Gesellschaft, 16 vols. (Berlin, 1907–22), iii.143

the repertory more quickly than its more som-bre counterpart and retained a dominant posi-tion there is something that Brahms himself noted wryly in a letter to his Berlin publisher Fritz Simrock in 1881: 'But I advise you to have the *Academic Overture* arranged for mil-itary band. I myself would be tempted by this if I knew anything more about it.'[10]

Klaus Döge
Translation: Stewart Spencer

---

[10] Kalbeck, *Johannes Brahms* (note 1), iii.266

VORWORT

Am 11. März 1879 verlieh die Friedrich-Wilhelms-Universität Breslau dem in Wien lebenden Komponisten Johannes Brahms die Ehrendoktorwürde. Das Diplom bezeichnete ihn als „artis musicae severioris in Germania nunc princeps"[1], als den jetzt ersten Tonsetzer der Kunst der strengeren Musik in Deutschland, und die Professorenschaft ging davon aus, dass Brahms sich für diese Ehrung auf musikalische Weise bedanken würde. Von einer Doktor-Symphonie oder einem feierlichen Gesang war dabei die Rede.[2] Doch verging über ein Jahr, bevor Brahms auf diese Erwartungen reagierte. Am 31. März 1880 schrieb er nach Breslau, er werde Anfang 1881 kommen, „zum Doktorschmaus mit Kegelschieben."[3]

Auch wenn entsprechende Belege fehlen, so dürfte er wohl zu diesem Zeitpunkt bereits erste Vorstellungen zu dem Bedankungswerk gehabt haben, das er dann während seiner Sommerferien 1880 in Bad Ischl im Salzkammergut komponierte und dem er den Titel *Akademische Festouvertüre* gab. Auffällig ist, dass er diesem Opus keine der ihm vertrauten Genres orchestralen Komponierens wie Serenade, Variation oder Symphonie zugrunde legte, sondern auf die in seinem Schaffen völlig neue Gattung der Konzert-Ouvertüre à la „Weber, Cherubini und Mendelssohn"[4] zurückgriff. Es handelte sich dabei um eine Gattung, die kompositorisch symphonischem Anspruch verpflichtet war, im Formalen aber eine gewisse Freiheit erlaubte. Gerade darin kam sie der Werkidee von Brahms entgegen; einer Werkidee, in deren Mittelpunkt das musikalische Zitieren von damals allbekannten Studentenliedern stand, was Brahms seinem Verleger gegenüber scherzhaft mit den

Worten beschrieb: „ein sehr lustiges Potpourri von Studentenliedern à la [Franz von] Suppé."[5]

Vier Liedmelodien, die er höchstwahrscheinlich dem in seinem Besitz befindlichen *Commers-Buch für den deutschen Studenten* von 1861 entnahm[6], hat Brahms benutzt:

1. Die Melodie des Studentenliedes „Wir hatten gebauet ein stattliches Haus" (episodenartig zitiert in den Takten 63ff.)

2. Den melodischen Mittelteil des Liedes „Alles schweige! Jeder neige ernsten Tönen nun sein Ohr!", in dem der Text lautet: „Hört, ich sing das Lied der Lieder" (verarbeitet im Seitensatz T. 129ff.)

3. Die Melodie des sogenannten Fuchsliedes „Was kommt dort von der Höh" (als Episode zitiert in T. 156ff.)

[1] Zitiert nach Max Kalbeck, *Johannes Brahms*, Bd. 3, zweite Auflage, Berlin 1912, S. 251–252.
[2] Kalbeck a. a. O., S. 251.
[3] Ebda.
[4] Ebda., S. 266, Anmerkung 31.
[5] Ebda, S. 266, Fußnote 19.
[6] Vgl. Christian Martin Schmidt, *Reclams Musikführer Johannes Brahms*, Stuttgart 1994, S. 82.

Lebhaft

Was kommt dort von der Höh', was kommt dort von der Höh'? was kommt dort von der le-der-nen Höh', ça ça le-der-nen Höh', was kommt dort von der Höh'?

4. Die Melodie des wohl bekanntesten Studentenliedes „Gaudeamus igitur" (in der Coda, T. 379ff., als Höhepunkt, „Maestoso", zitiert)

Feierlich

Gau-de-a-mus i-gi-tur, ju-ve-nes dum su – mus; post ju-cun-dum ju-ven-tu-tem, post mo-les-tam se-nec-tu-tem nos ha-be-bit hu – mus, nos ha-be-bit hu – mus.

Natürlich macht diese Werkidee, die weniger den hehren Anlass der von den Fakultäts-Magnifizenzen und der Professorenschaft verliehenen Ehrendoktorwürde als vielmehr das lustige Studentenleben im Auge zu haben scheint, auf den ersten Blick stutzig, und schon Kalbeck schrieb in seiner Brahms-Biographie:

Äußerlich betrachtet, könnte die Ouvertüre, welche die Studenten näher angeht als die Professoren, für eine Eulenspiegelei des allem Formelkram und Perückenwesen gründlich abholden Meisters betrachtet werden. Keinesfalls ist der Gedanke ausgeschlossen, daß der endlich gewaltsam unter den Doktorhut gebrachte Brahms sich nicht nebenbei ein Späßchen mit den hochwohlweisen, im Ornat aufmarschierenden Herren Professoren erlauben wollte, und der Gedanke, sie in den Konzertsaal zu zitieren, um sie dort zum Fuchsritt antreten zu lassen und mit dem „Gaudeamus" heimzuschicken, wäre seinem Schelmensinn wohl zuzutrauen gewesen.[7]

Auf den zweiten Blick aber finden sich doch mögliche Anspielungen auf den eigentlichen Anlass. So könnte der damals jedem geläufige Textanfang des von Brahms für das erste Zitat ausgesuchten Liedes („Wir hatten gebauet ein stattliches Haus") sich durchaus auf die Neugründung und den wissenschaftlichen Ausbau der Breslauer Universität durch die Zusammenlegung der alten Leopoldina mit der Frankfurter (Oder) Viadrina im Jahre 1811 beziehen. Des Weiteren könnte jenes zweite Liedzitat „Alles schweiget", aus dem Brahms für seinen Seitensatz nur diejenigen originalen Töne übernahm, die über den Worten „Hört, ich sing das Lied der Lieder" stehen, als eine gewisse Dankesgeste des für die Musik des op. 80 verantwortlichen Komponisten verstanden werden; und vielleicht war es für den hymnenartigen Abschluss gar nicht die erste Strophe des Liedes „Gaudeamus igitur", an die Brahms bei der Zitierung dachte, sondern dessen vierte, in der es heißt: „Die Akademie möge leben, die Professoren mögen leben, es lebe jedes Mitglied und alle Abteilungen, immer sollen sie in Blüte stehen."[8]

Die erfolgreiche Uraufführung des Opus 80 fand am 4. Januar 1881 unter Brahms' Leitung in Breslau statt, wobei auch ihr Gegenstück, die *Tragische Ouvertüre* op. 81 erklang, zwei Ouvertüren aus derselben Zeit, die zwei Seiten des Komponisten Brahms zeigten: „(Die eine weint, die andre lacht)".[9] Dass dabei die „Lachende" schneller und nachhaltiger als die „Weinende" Eingang in das allgemeine Konzertrepertoire fand, hat Brahms 1881 dem Berliner Verleger Fritz Simrock mit einem seiner üblichen Scherze kommentiert: „Die Akademische empfehle ich Ihnen aber für Militärmusik setzen zu lassen. Das lockt mich selbst, wenn ich nur genauer damit Bescheid wüßte."[10]

Klaus Döge

7 Kalbeck, a. a. O., S. 252.

8 Übersetzung vom Verfasser nach der Wiedergabe des lateinischen Originals in: *Buch der Lieder. 262 beliebte Volksweisen aus alter und neuer Zeit*, ausgewählt und bearbeitet von L. Benda, Braunschweig, o. J. [ca. 1910]. [Nach dieser Quelle auch die Notenbeispiele und Liedtexte]

9 So Brahms im Brief an Carl Reinecke vom 7. Oktober 1880, in: *Brahms-Briefwechsel* Bd. III, a. a. O., S. 143.

10 Kalbeck, a. a. O. S. 266.

PRÉFACE

Le 11 mars 1879, Brahms se vit décerner un doctorat honoraire de l'Université Friedrich Wilhelm de Breslau. La distinction décrivit le compositeur qui, à ce moment-là, vivait à Vienne comme « artis musicae severioris in Germania nunc princeps » (« Principal représentant à ce jour de l'art de la musique sérieuse en Allemagne »)[1], les autorités professorales attendant à l'évidence du compositeur ainsi flatté une expression de sa gratitude face à l'honneur qui lui avait été fait. On parla même d'une « symphonie doctorale » ou d'une cantate festive.[2] En fait, plus d'une année s'écoula avant que Brahms ne satisfît leur espoir et ce n'est que le 31 mai 1880 qu'il écrivit à l'Université pour annoncer sa venue à Breslau au début de l'année suivante « pour un carrousel doctoral accompagné d'un jeu de quilles. »[3]

Même si l'on ne dispose d'aucun document appuyant cette théorie, il semble vraisemblable qu'à cette date Brahms eût déjà en tête certaines idées sur la nouvelle œuvre qu'il commença à noter pendant ses vacances d'été à Bad Ischl (province de Salzkammergut). Singulièrement pour une œuvre qu'il intitula *Ouverture pour une festivité académique*, Brahms ne recourut à aucune des formes qui lui étaient familières comme la sérénade, les variations ou la symphonie, mais se tourna plutôt vers la structure totalement inédite pour lui de l'ouverture de concert « à la Weber, Chérubini et Mendelssohn. »[4] Cette forme, qui tout en entretenant des ambitions symphoniques laissait au compositeur une certaine liberté, coïncidait avec l'idée que se faisait Brahms de cette nouvelle partition et de l'importance essentielle que devait y prendre les citations musicales de chansons d'étudiants connues de tous à cette époque. C'est ce que Brahms décrivit sur le ton de la plaisanterie dans une lettre à son éditeur dans laquelle il

parle de la pièce comme d'« un joyeux pot-pourri de chansons d'étudiants à la Suppé. »[5]

Brahms choisit quatre mélodies de chansons, presque sûrement sélectionnées dans l'édition de 1861 du *Commers-Buch für den deutschen Studenten* (Livre des chansons à boire des étudiants allemands) dont il possédait un exemplaire :[6] (1) l'air de la chanson *Wir hatten gebauet ein stattliches Haus* (Nous avions construit une maison magnifique), cité épisodiquement dans les mesures 63 et suivantes :

(2) la partie centrale de la chanson *Alles schweige ! Jeder neige ernsten Tönen nun sein Ohr !* (Faisons tous silence ! Que chacun prête une oreille à des airs plus sérieux !), qui comprend les mots *Hört, ich sing das Lied der Lieder* (Ecoutez, je chante le chant des chants) développés dans la présentation du deuxième thème des mesures 129 et suivantes :

Cité in: Max Kalbeck, *Johannes Brahms*, 4 volumes, 2e 2d., Berlin, 1912, iii. p.251–252
[   ] Kalbeck, *Johannes Brahms* (note 1), iii. p. 251
[   ] Kalbeck, *Johannes Brahms* (note 1), iii. p. 251
[   ] Kalbeck, *Johannes Brahms* (note 1), iii. p. 266, note 31

[5] Kalbeck, *Johannes Brahms* (note 1), iii. p. 266, note 19
[6] Voir Christian Martin Schmidt, *Reclams Musikführer Johannes Brahms*, Stuttgart, 1994, p. 82

(3) la mélodie de la chanson des nouveaux arrivants *Was kommt dort von der Höh'?* (qu'est-ce qui tombe ici du ciel ?), citée épisodiquement dans les mesures 156 et suivantes :

(4) la mélodie de *Gaudeamus igitur*, incontestablement la plus célèbre des chansons d'étudiants allemandes, citée à l'apogée de la cadence dans les mesures 379 et suivantes (*Maestoso*) :

Cette idée fondatrice semble moins s'appliquer à une cérémonie solennelle au cours de laquelle les recteurs de la faculté et les membres de son corps professoral allaient remettre un doctorat honoraire au compositeur que décrire les aspects plus insouciants de la vie estudiantine. De prime abord, elle intrigue et fit même écrire Max Kalbeck dans sa biographie de Brahms :

Superficiellement, l'ouverture, qui s'adresse plus aux étudiants qu'à leurs professeurs, peut être considérée comme une plaisanterie jouée par un compositeur fondamentalement opposé à toute absurdité stéréotypée et emperruquée. On ne peut donc pas exclure que le compositeur, finalement obligé de revêtir la coiffe et la toge, se soit autorisé une farce aux dépens des professeurs émérites s'avançant sur la scène dans tout leur apparat. La pensée de les rassembler dans la salle de fêtes et de leur présenter les accents de la chanson d'un nouvel arrivant avant de les renvoyer avec *Gaudeamus igitur* résonnant à leurs oreilles n'est en aucun cas hors de question, étant donné son sens espiègle de l'humour.[7]

Toutefois, une analyse plus approfondie révèle des allusions potentielles à l'occasion pour laquelle elle fut composée. Ainsi, par exemple, le vers initial de la chanson choisie par Brahms pour sa première citation et familier à tout auditeur contemporain – « Nous avions construit une maison magnifique » – pourrait-il faire référence au ré-établissement et à l'agrandissement de l'Université de Breslau à la suite de la fusion des anciennes universités Leopoldina et Viadrina de Francfort-sur-l'Oder en 1811, tandis que la deuxième citation – « Faisons tous silence ! » – dont Brahms n'emprunta que la mélodie originale des mots « Ecoutez, je chante le chant des chants » pour son deuxième thème – pourrait être interprétée comme un geste de gratitude de la part du compositeur de l'ouverture. Enfin, Brahms n'avait peut-être pas tant en tête la strophe initiale de *Gaudeamus igitur* quand il choisit cette chanson pour la conclusion en forme d'hymne de son ouverture que sa quatrième strophe et les vers: « Vivat academia / Vivant professores / Vivat membrum quodlibet / Vivat membra quaelibet / Semper sint in flore » (Vive l'académie / Vive les professeurs / Vive chaque membre et chaque faculté / Qu'ils fleurissent à jamais.)[8]

L'Opus 80 de Brahms fut triomphalement créé à Breslau le 4 janvier 1881 sous sa direction. Le programme comprenait aussi l'*Ouverture tragique*, Op. 81, pièce-compagne de l'*Ouverture pour une festivité académique*. Ces deux œuvres contemporaines dévoilent des aspects opposés de la personnalité du compositeur – « L'une pleure, l'autre rit. »[9] Brahms lui-même releva

[7] Kalbeck, *Johannes Brahms* (note 1), iii. p. 252
[8] L. Benda (éditeur), *Buch der Lieder; 262 beliebte Volkweisen aus alter und neuer Zeit*, Braunschweig, s. d. [ca 1910]
[9] Ainsi Brahms dans une lettre à Carl Reinecke du 7 octobre 1880; voir *Johannes Brahms Briefwechsel*, éd. Deutsche Brahms-Gesellschaft, 16 volumes, Berlin, 1907-1922, iii. p. 143

avec un humour forcé le fait que l'ouverture exprimant le rire soit entrée plus rapidement au répertoire que sa contrepartie plus grave et y ait gardé une position dominante dans une lettre adressée à son éditeur Fritz Simrock à Berlin en 1881: « Je vous conseille néanmoins de faire arranger l'*Ouverture académique* pour fanfare militaire. Je serais moi-même tenté de le faire si je m'y connaissais mieux. »[10]

Klaus Döge
Traduction: Agnès Ausseur

---

[10] Kalbeck, *Johannes Brahms* (note 1), iii. p. 266

AKADEMISCHE FESTOUVERTÜRE

Johannes Brahms
(1833–1897)
Op. 80

Edited by Richard Clarke
© 2010 Ernst Eulenburg Ltd, London
and Ernst Eulenburg & Co. GmbH, Mainz

L'istesso tempo, un poco maestoso

Maestoso (♩ = ♩)